LEAF

A true life story for children.

By Andrew Bickerton

Illustrations by Sue Kingston

ISBN 978-1-999 8156-7-7

Printed by Biddles Books, King's Lynn, Norfolk PE32 1SF

In the middle of a village green stood a tall tree.

The tree had stood there for as long as anyone could remember.

At the top of this tree, at the end of a branch and at the very tip of a twig, was a little bud.

It was spring and this little bud was about to burst into life.

But this little bud had to face many dangers…

First there were the pigeons.

The pigeons loved to eat tender young buds and many were gobbled up before they could open.

But our little bud was at the end of a long, thin twig and try as they might the pigeons could not reach her.

Then, when the sun warmed and the rain came, the buds burst into leaf. These fresh green leaves were a delicious lunch for caterpillars and they busily munched their way from leaf to leaf and from branch to branch.

As our little bud was at the very top of the tree she was the last to open. But when at last she opened she saw many other leaves had been eaten away and some fat caterpillars were crawling towards her. In a few hours she would be eaten!

What could she do?

She could not run away as she had no legs. She had no wings so she could not fly away.

She waited and waited and the hungry, fat caterpillars came closer and closer and closer and then…

With a flap and a flutter little birds with blue hats and yellow jerseys landed on her branch and each snatched a beak full of caterpillars and flew away.

After a short time the birds returned and took some more caterpillars

and then some more

and then some more

until there were no caterpillars left.

Leaf was safe!

Weeks went by and the days grew longer and warmer. Beautiful scented flowers appeared all around her. There came a loud buzzing. Bees had come to visit the flowers. They buzzed to and fro, to and fro visiting each blossom in turn.

Leaf dozed happily in the gentle breeze listening to the buzzing bees and life for Leaf was perfect.

Day after day the blossoms were visited by the bees until one by one the petals dropped from the flowers and the bees no longer came to visit.

Leaf was sad to lose her busy friends. The flowers had gone as well but small pods with wings were growing where the blossom used to be.

How strange! What could they be?

The summer sun grew stronger and the days grew longer. Leaf was visited again by the birds with blue hats. This time they brought their children as well.

The birds were very friendly and their chattering and chirping kept her amused. She enjoyed watching the children's attempts at flying.

Then one day the little birds could fly and off they all flew, chirping their goodbyes as they left.

Leaf was alone again!

Some days were now very frightening for Leaf. Strong winds dashed her from side to side and some nights thunderstorms crashed and flashed and shook the whole tree like an angry giant.

The branches were shaken from side to side and many leaves lost their grip and were blown far away.

One day, when a strong wind was blowing, all the pods started to be blown away too. Leaf watched as each seed with its special wing twirled round and round in a joyful dance as it was carried along on the breeze.

Leaf wished that she too might fly away.

She wished that she wasn't stuck to the tree.

She wanted to be like the birds.

She wanted to be like the bees

and she wanted to be like the spinning, dancing pods.

She wanted to be free!

Week by week the summer faded to autumn.

Fewer birds were skimming above and fewer songs were heard in the tree tops.

Leaf began to feel tired and she noticed that all the green leaves surrounding her were changing to brown and gold. Many leaves lay on the ground beneath her.

The nights grew longer and colder.

Leaf shivered under the starlit sky.

One cold and windy morning she woke to see hundreds of leaves flying away on the wind.

Her own grip on the twig

weakened and she too

was blown into the air.

As she was at the very top of the tree she had a very long way to fall.

The wind caught her and she sailed away, flying like a bird and spinning round and round like the seed pods.

This was fun!

She landed at last and settled gently on the grass.

Leaf found herself in a completely different world.

She looked up and saw her tree standing bare against the sky.

Not a leaf was left on her tree.

It looked so sad.

And then, one bright and breezy day, a puff of wind picked her up and off she went,

leaping and dancing, whirling and twirling across the frosty grass

and along the road

until she was blown under a thick hedge.

She was exhausted.

Lying under the hedge Leaf found lots and lots of other leaves from her tree and also, to her surprise and delight, some of the small, winged seed pods.

There she remained for the rest of the winter sheltering from the rain, wind, ice and snow, making a thick warm blanket with the other leaves.

After many weeks the days grew longer and warmer and, from under the blanket of dead leaves, a new green shoot appeared growing towards the welcoming sun.

The life of Leaf had ended but, with her help, the life of a new tree had only just begun….

THE BEGINNING!

WHAT DO YOU KNOW ABOUT TREES?

The tree that Leaf grew on is called a sycamore. It is a deciduous tree with scented blossoms and twirling seed pods.

There are **deciduous and evergreen trees.**

Deciduous trees lose their leaves in the autumn. Evergreen trees do not lose their leaves.

A lot of evergreen trees are conifers. They have fir cones and needles instead of leaves.

The Christmas tree is an evergreen. It has needles instead of leaves.

Trees are very important for our planet. They help to keep the air clean so that we can breathe.

Trees help to shade us from the sun. They also protect us from strong winds.

Trees provide wood for our heating and wood for making furniture and building houses.

Fallen leaves help to feed new plants and the leaves make a compost to put in our gardens.

QUIZ AND ACTIVITIES.

- What is the name of Leaf's tree?

- What type of tree is it?

- What birds try to eat the buds?

- How is Leaf saved from the caterpillars?

- Why do the bees come to Leaf's tree?

- What is special about a Sycamore's seeds?

- What happens to the colour of leaves in the autumn?

- Find out the names of other trees that lose their leaves in autumn and see if you know what sort of seeds they have.

- Name some trees that provide us with food.

- Why not make a collection of different leaves?

- Go for a walk in a wood in spring time. Do the same walk in autumn. What differences do you notice?

About the Author

Andrew Bickerton is a retired English teacher living in a small village in Norfolk, England. He has written and directed many amateur dramatic productions but this is his first children's book. "The environment, nature and wildlife are very important to me and their preservation for future generations to enjoy one of my main concerns."

My thanks to Sue Kingston for her patience in producing the delightful illustrations.